'A So

Pe

to ac
Edin                          ...rary

by

**Sally Wood**

Edinburgh
Edinburgh University Library
1985

A Sort of Dignified Flippancy

Penguin Books 1935-1960

to accompany the collection in
Edinburgh University Library

Betty Ward

Edinburgh
Edinburgh Bibliographical Society
1985

# Acknowledgements

I would like to thank firstly Peter B. Freshwater and Murray Simpson both of Edinburgh University Library, for the helpful advice given in the formation of the booklet. Secondly I am extremely grateful to Mr George Gibb and Dr Angus Mitchell who so readily lent me from their own private collections anything that I requested and provided other books that they thought I should see. I would also like to acknowledge the help given by the Friends of Edinburgh University Library, especially Miss A.B.G. Dunlop, Mrs Betsy Uldall, Mrs A. Redfern, Miss Phyllis Downie and Dr A. Wilson who all donated, so eagerly, titles that our collection lacked. Lastly, I would like to thank the Publications Department in Edinburgh University Library for typing my notorious writing into 'machine readable form' and David Stewart-Robinson and Pam Armstrong of the Reprographics Unit of Edinburgh Regional Computing Centre for their assistance.

# Contents

# Contents

# Precursors

On 30th July 1935 Allen Lane published the first ten Penguins. No-one then could have foretold the far-reaching consequences of this event. Today 'Penguin' has for some people become synonymous with the word, paperback, and over fifty per cent of all books produced are in this soft cover format.

Allen Lane was by no means the first to issue books with paper covers. These can be traced as far back as the early 16th century. However, the most significant stages began in the 19th century under the famous name of Tauchnitz.

Christian Bernhard Tauchnitz (1816-1895) commenced publishing in Leipzig on 1st February 1837 under the business name of 'Bern. Tauchnitz, Jnr.' In 1841 he announced the publication of his bestseller series of reprints of British and later American authors, under the generic name 'Collection of British Authors'. He included a statement that all interested authors would be paid for the rights to publish their works, even though this was unnecessary under the law at that time. These books were low-priced editions of titles by modern authors; Macaulay and Thackeray were two of the most popular authors used. The first title published was Bulwer-Lytton's "Pelham" and the earliest known paperback edition still in existence is No. 138 of 1847, Lever's "Harry Lorrequer". Each Tauchnitz edition carried the following piece of information: 'Not to be introduced into the British Empire' and later 'or the United States of America'. This meant that, as soon as any were brought into these countries, they immediately became smuggled books, and liable to confiscation by the British Customs. For almost one hundred years the Tauchnitz Edition held the cheap paperback market and their Tauchnitz books were found in almost all Continental bookshops and railway bookstalls. They had agents in every European country and many of the bookshops had English-speaking staff, as did W.H. Smith & Son, 248 Rue de Rivoli, Paris, and it was Paris, rather than Leipzig, that became the principal market. However, though these books were extremely successful (5,000 titles were issued by 1932), the public did not at any time acquire a superior design when they bought a Tauchnitz. The paper quality was poor as was the typography and the pages were uncut. The paper covers, a dirty white with black lettering, were drab and monotonous and were too wide and long to fit into travellers' pockets. Tauchnitz eventually merged with Albatross in 1936 and this 'anschluss' was destroyed in 1943 by an air-raid that lasted from 3rd to 4th December. In 1946, as Tauchnitz Gmbh Edition, it resurfaced in Hamburg with Christian Wegner as managing director and then it moved to Stuttgart from 1952 until 1955. Between 1946 and 1955 the Tauchnitz Edition New Series 101-140 was issued and it finally ended in 1973 when the firm was struck off the register because of lack of capital.

Two other German collections are worth a mention here. Firstly there was Reclam's Universal-Bibliothek which is still in existence today. These were successful cheap paperback reprints of well-known authors such as Goethe, Schiller and Ibsen. The design is little changed today apart from the Gothic script which is no longer used. It was their proud boast that "once a title was published it remained in print evermore". Secondly there was the English Library published by F.A. Brockhaus in Leipzig and Hachette and Co in Paris, both of which printed books in the English language. These had charming illustrated picture paper covers and had the same distribution restrictions as Tauchnitz editions.

In England Benn's Sixpenny Library (edited initially by William Rose and later by Victor Gollancz) was selling well. These were smaller than pocket size with a rather dull design using the colours brown and buff. They were printed on poor quality paper and were typographically unimaginative. Each one carried the words that it had 'the revolutionary aim of providing a reference library to the best modern thought written by the foremost authorities at the price of 6d. a volume'. The Cassells National Library, 1885-1890, whose editor was Professor Henry Morley, published weekly volumes of popular literature priced at 3d. Hodder and Stoughton Yellow Jackets began around February 1926. They were fiction, priced at 9d, and had a pictorial cover

Tauchnitz Edition Vol 4195
Leipzig 1910

The Albatross Vol. 66
Hamburg 1933

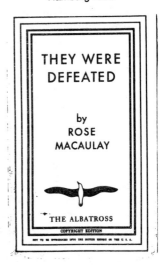

TAUCHNITZ EDITION
COLLECTION OF BRITISH AND AMERICAN AUTHORS
VOL. 4195

# THE EGOIST

BY

## G. MEREDITH

IN TWO VOLUMES

VOL. 2

LEIPZIG: BERNHARD TAUCHNITZ
PARIS: LIBRAIRIE HENRI GAULON, 39, RUE MADAME

The Copyright of this Collection is purchased for Continental Circulation
only, and the volumes may therefore not be introduced into Great Britain
or her Colonies. (See also pp. 3–6 of Large Catalogue.)

EACH VOLUME SOLD SEPARATELY

THEY WERE
DEFEATED

by
ROSE
MACAULAY

THE ALBATROSS

COPYRIGHT EDITION

NOT TO BE INTRODUCED INTO THE BRITISH EMPIRE OR THE U. S. A.

*Tauchnitz Edition*

## THE LUDWIGS
## OF BAVARIA

*by*

*Henry Channon*

*Leipzig · Hamburg · Paris*

MICROBE
HUNTERS

by
PAUL DE KRUIF

THE ALBATROSS

AUTHORIZED EDITION

NOT TO BE INTRODUCED INTO THE BRITISH EMPIRE OR THE U. S. A.

Tauchnitz Edition Vol 5126
Leipzig 1937

The Albatross Ltd.
London and Paris 1947

with a yellow background. The back cover almost always displayed an advertisement for the Prudential Assurance Co Ltd. Around 1937 they began publishing editions featuring crosswords concerning the book's content. However the cheapest available were, in Scotland, the Pennyworth Series published by Morison Brothers of Glasgow, and, in London, the Penny Popular Novels (edited by W.T. Stead) which were mainly abridged and could be found on most railway bookstalls.

F.J. Sheed and Maisie Ward started their Roman Catholic publishing house in London in 1926, assisted by T.F. Burns. They issued paperbacks on mainly theological and philosophical subjects, easily recognisable by their bright yellow covers stamped with the words *Cheap Editions* 1/8d. or 2/6d. In 1938, in an attempt to match the success of Penguin, Sheed and Ward created a new series called Unicorn Books, attractively designed with pale green covers and the logo of a Unicorn on the front cover. However only twelve were ever published, between November 1938 and September 1939, and both these series disappeared after the disastrous German bomb raid of 31st December 1940, which gutted most of London's publishing houses including Sheed and Ward's offices and warehouses.

In 1932 in Hamburg a modern paperback was introduced by a publisher called John Holroyd-Reece, backed by a consortium of British publishers including Kurt Enoch, later of USA Penguin fame.It was this new paperback, the Albatross, designed by the famous Veronese typographer Giovanni Mardersteig which had the most influence on Allen Lane when he created his Penguin books. These attractive volumes, though still not pocket size, were the first to have different coloured paper covers to specify subject categories. However, Europe was not large enough to handle two publishing houses producing English authors and after the 1936 consolidation with Tauchnitz, the name disappeared for a number of years. The new Tauchnitz edition that emerged, used all the Albatross principles including the addition of vertical coloured stripes on the covers, signifying the book's content – red for crime, blue for love stories, green for travel, etc. In 1947 and 1948, four years after the disastrous

**Benn's Sixpenny Library No 93**
**London 1929**

**Reclams Universal– Bibliothek**
**2309**

Cassell's National Library 1887

Penny Popular Novels No 40

Leipzig bomb raid some Albatross titles reappeared alongside Tauchnitz Gmbh. The original self-coloured paper covers were re-used and the only difference was the imprint – The Albatross Ltd., London and Paris. 'Hamburg, Paris and Bologna' was deleted from the front cover and 'copyright edition' was substituted by 'authorised edition' . This revival like Tauchnitz was short-lived.

These were the main precursors of Allen Lane's Penguin kingdom, along with the Insel-Bucherei of the Insel Verlag, which had such special significance for the King Penguin Series and which will be mentioned later.

## The First Ten Titles

In London on 21st September 1902 Allen Lane Williams was born. His father was an architect and his mother came from a farming family. He had an unspectacular scholastic career at Bristol Grammar School before leaving in 1919. A distant relative of his mother, John Lane, owned the Bodley Head publishing house and, as he had no children of his own, he was afraid that the family name would die out. He agreed to take Allen into the firm as heir apparent with one condition, that he adopted his surname. On the 16th April 1919 the Williams family changed their name to Lane by deed poll, and the Allen Lane legend was launched. On 23rd April 1919 he joined the Bodley Head as a representative and it was in those early years that he established his publishing contacts. His uncle died at the age of 67 in 1925, at which time his firm was steadily going downhill. Allen had been promoted to the Bodley Head board the previous year and over the next few years he became the majority shareholder and the managing director. However, apart from procuring the British rights to James Joyce's Ulysses, he achieved little else of note as a publisher until 1935, the 'Year of the Penguin'. As J E Morpurgo states 'Allen Lane dreamed up Penguin to save the Bodley Head, but the Bodley Head refused to be saved' and eventually in 1937 the company went into voluntary liquidation.

It was after a weekend spent with Agatha Christie and her second husband, the archaeologist Max Mallowan, that the Penguin book was created. Allen Lane found himself at Exeter Station waiting for a train, and could find nothing at the bookstall to read to pass the time. He spent the next hour mulling over an idea that had lain dormant for a number of years. Many people he knew bemoaned the fact that it was only at European railway bookstalls that cheap reprints could be bought for the public to read. What if Bodley Head published a new series introducing reprints of quality fiction and non-fiction and sold it to the public at the ridiculous price of 6d, the price of ten cigarettes? That concept combines all ideas of the inaugural series: the sixpenny idea of Benn's Library, the cheap paperback edition of Sheed and

Ward, Tauchnitz and others, the refinement of the Albatross design, their use of colour categories, and their idea of producing books for the general reader and the scholar. Allen Lane took this prototype even further with the revolutionary ideas of mass production and distribution and mass media advertising. In essence what Woolworth's had already achieved with their 6d. stalls in hardware, he wanted to achieve in the book world. Naturally the Bodley Head board was sceptical as was the rest of the book trade, all of whom forecast total failure. In the end Allen Lane decided to go ahead alone, and eventually his two brothers Dick and John were won round by his persuasive arguments. Together they tried to think of a name for the new series:it had to be friendly, happy, not too scholarly, and a name that would appeal to everyone. Dolphin was one of the first suggestions, as it appears in the Bristol coat of arms, but it was rejected on the grounds that it was a name already heavily used. They eventually decided on Penguin because it had 'a sort of dignified flippancy', and Edward Young, a junior in the Bodley Head, was sent to the zoo to sketch penguins.The famous Penguin logo had arrived.

On Tuesday 30th July 1935, ten new titles appeared in the bookshops of London, bright colourful books that immediately drew the attention of the public: orange for fiction, green for crime, red for plays, dark blue for biography, yellow for miscellaneous, cerise for travel. Numbers 1-10 of the new reprints series were as follows:

1. *Ariel* by Andre Maurois      (Dark blue)
2. *A Farewell to Arms* by Ernest Hemingway      (Orange)
3. *Poets Pub* by Eric Linklater      (Orange)
4. *Madame Claire* by Susan Ertz      (Orange)
5. *Unpleasantness at the Bellona Club*
   by Dorothy L Sayers      (Green)
6. *The Mysterious Affair at Styles*
   by Agatha Christie      (Green)
   (This book reappeared as No. 61 on its third reprint in July 1936, while No. 6 was allocated to the first reprint of *The Murder on the Links* by Agatha Christie. When the latter

**Penguin Books No 1 July 1935**

**First Pelican Book (A1) May 1937**

was first published in March 1936, its number was 6A, and it has now become a highly sought after book.)

7. *Twenty-five* by Beverley Nichols                (Dark blue)
8. *William* by E H Young                                    (Orange)
9. *Gone to Earth* by Mary Webb                      (Orange)
10. *Carnival* by Compton Mackenzie               (Orange)
    (Eventually withdrawn because the author had already sold the copyright.)

These were an immediate success, not only in the bookshops, but throughout the country in every Woolworth store. (They have now been reprinted in facsimile to celebrate the 50th anniversary of their publication.) Allen Lane had initiated a new market for books by approaching Woolworth who, after a fortnight's hesitation had placed a pre-publication consignment order of 63,500 copies. The indecision was not because of the price, but reflected understandable doubts as to whether Woolworth's was the best place for a biography on Shelley to make its first appearance. Clifford Prescott, the managing director of Woolworth had no cause to regret his historic decision, because Allen Lane's wider range of title catered for as many tastes as possible. On 1st January 1936 Penguin Books Ltd was founded with £100 capital, but the imprint of "The Bodley Head" continued to be used until Penguin No 79 was published in 1937. The sales that followed exceeded all expectations and in order to cope with the distribution Allen Lane was forced to take over the crypt of the Holy Trinity Church in Marylebone Road that had been used as a Bodley Head overflow store. The conditions there would have had every trade union today up in arms! There was no sanitation, just a pail for the men, who all took their turn in emptying it! The girls on the staff were given 6d. extra a week to use the public lavatories at Great Portland Street. It was in this crypt that Eunice Frost began her career, eventually becoming a director and a key member of the editorial committee. There were two empty tombs which when fitted with locked metal doors were used for invoicing stationery and a safe. A chute which ran from the graveyard above and an electrically operated hoist, the only modern innovation, were the transporters of books. These conditions lasted until 1937 when, after a plague of mice, complaints reached epidemic proportions about the odour of the stock arriving in bookshops. Even today some collectors say they can tell whether they have an early Penguin by the smell of it! Allen Lane showed his forward thinking by moving out of London and buying a three-acre plot at Harmondsworth in Middlesex, only 15 miles from Hyde Park. At that time no major publisher was housed outside London. Many were envious of Allen's foresight when most publishing houses lost their premises and complete bookstocks during the bombing of London between 1940 and 1944. Allen Lane's father laid the foundation stone at Harmondsworth on 4 August 1937.

# Penguin Books Progress

In April 1937 the first six Penguin Shakespeares arrived, a series which was discontinued during the War and was eventually completed in 1959. However it was in the next month of 1937 that the most decisive move to secure Penguin Book's future occurred. Allen Lane had had a letter from George Bernard Shaw in 1936 congratulating him on his Penguin series and suggesting a title which he might have been interested in publishing. Always an opportunist, Allen wrote back saying he would try but he would much prefer to have the rights to Shaw's "Intelligent Woman's Guide to Socialism, Capitalism and Sovietism". Shaw agreed terms with incredible celerity and moreover offered to write two original chapters for the book. Allen decided this warranted a new series, a series that would introduce didactic titles to the public, and the name Pelican was chosen because frequently letters arrived in London erroneously addressed to Pelican Books. The first Pelicans were reprints of works by such distinguished names as Sir Julian Huxley, Sir Leonard Woolley and Elie Halevy. However, because he realised he did not have enough experience in the academic world, Allen called in V. Krishna Menon as chief editor. He introduced the Lane brothers to W.E. Williams, who was at that time the secretary of the British Institute of Adult Education, and, H.L. Beales of the University of London, and they became advisory members of the editorial board. Pelicans became a library of modern knowledge used not only by people craving learning, but also as standard textbooks by students of universities and institutes of higher education.

In November of the same year, another major series was created. The Penguin and Pelican Specials began as a current affairs series to inform the public of the political scene in Britain and the rest of Europe, and soon became handbooks and authoritative guides to current politics and social history. One of the most recent is M. Crick's "Scargill and the Miners", but it was in February 1938 that the series broke new ground for Penguin Books Ltd. No 1 had been a reprint by Edgar Mowrer, "Germany puts the Clock back", but numbers 2 and 3, G.T. Garratt's "Mussolini's Roman Empire" and Genevieve Tabouis', "Blackmail or War" were specially commissioned for the series. Thereafter, new titles, as opposed to reprints, took more and more space on the publishing schedules. During the war 155 Specials were published and today these remain interesting contemporary historical analyses.

Penguin Parade No 1 was published as Penguin No 120 in November 1937 but then became a serial in its own right. Fourteen numbers altogether were published and though it began as an outlet for lesser-known authors it changed its content with No 11 and became almost a modern studies type of journal. The last part was published in 1948.

Penguin Books issued another series in May 1938 that had a short life-span. Numbers 1-10 of Illustrated Classics, the only ones ever to be published, were ex-copyright titles like Daniel Defoe's "Robinson Crusoe" (C6 and C7) and Jonathan Swift's "Gulliver's Travels" (C10). However these authors had been overproduced in hardback series such as "Everyman" and "The World's Classics" which meant that they did not sell well as a Penguin paperback. This was Penguin Books' first venture into illustrated books and, although their delightful wood engravings were drawn by such famous artists as Robert Gibbings and Ethelbert White, the shape and size of the Penguin Book (18cm x 11cm) did not really do justice to these illustrations. They were discontinued in that same year and other titles destined for that series were subsequently issued in the 'miscellaneous' yellow Penguin cover. These included Izaak Walton's "The Compleat Angler" (238), Gilbert White's "The Natural History of Selbourne" (296), and Edward Lear's "A Book of Lear" (234).

In March 1939 the Penguin Guides began with the issue of Vols 1-6 under the editorship of L. Russell Muirhead, editor of the Blue Guides. It was intended to cover all the counties of England and Wales, but when War broke out, there seemed no point in continuing them. In March 1946, Vol 7 by W.T. Palmer on the Lake District appeared and Nos 1-6 were revised and reprinted at one shilling each. With an 8-page atlas of Bartholomew's

## TWELFTH NIGHT

THE PENGUIN SHAKESPEARE

EDITED BY G. B. HARRISON

# PENGUIN PARADE

NEW STORIES, POEMS, ETC., BY CONTEMPORARY WRITERS
FIRST ENGLISH PUBLICATION

## 2

JOHNNY PYE AND THE FOOL-KILLER
....................................... Stephen Vincent Benet
ANDALUSIAN RHAPSODY .................. Guy Dent
EVERYTHING IN THE WINDOW ....... I. A. R. Wylie
THE CHRIST CHILD .................... Fred Urquhart
A CHINESE VASE ....................... R. Gibbons
COPY ................................. Gwyn Jones
THE ANIMALS' FAIR .................... J. G. Cozzens
ABDICATION ........................... Sidney Young
PEAT ................................. Edgar Howard
BOANERGES ............................ G. W. Galwey
"FROM NATURAL CAUSES" ................ Owen Rutter
HARPS UPON THE WILLOWS ............... Joseph Vogel
THE CURÉ'S BOOTS ..................... George Bellairt

POEMS by Andrew Young and A. S. J. Tessimond

ILLUSTRATIONS by Beryl Edwards, Gertrude Hermes,
John Oldag

PENGUIN ILLUSTRATED CLASSICS

# SOME TALES OF MYSTERY & IMAGINATION

## POE

Wood-engravings by Douglas Percy Bliss

## THE PENGUIN NEW WRITING

REPORT ON TO-DAY

| | |
|---|---|
| Eric de Maury | A Night in the Country |
| Rosamond Lehmann | Wonderful Holidays—III |
| H. R. Savage | Night Attack |
| F. J. Salfeld | The Gregole |

| | |
|---|---|
| A. S. J. Tessimond | Two Poems |
| Daniel George | The Eagle |
| Robert Medley | Egypt |
| Kenneth Lo | A Chinese Seaman |
| Terence Tiller | A Story by Maupassant |
| Frank O'Connor | Three Poems |
| David Luke | Three Poems |
| T. C. Worsley | The Mackenzies |
| Harry Brown | Castel di Sangro |
| Peter Viertal | Smudge |
| Dance Critic | Three British Choreographers |

BOOK FRONT

| | |
|---|---|
| Kenneth Muir | Three Hundred Years of Milton's Poems |
| Stephen Spender | Prescriptions for a Modern Masterpiece |
| John Lehmann | State Art and Scepticism |
| | Photogravure Illustrations |
| | From a Painter's Notebook—I |

EDITED BY
JOHN LEHMANN

NUMBER 24          NINEPENCE

maps, each was designed for the hiker, cyclist and motorist. A new series, compiled by F.R. Banks began in 1955 with G14 and this time included titles such as "Warwickshire and the Shakespeare Country" and "London". The series was discontinued in 1956 without having crossed the Scottish Border.

## King Penguins

The King Penguin series began in November 1939, and at last publishers were made to realise that Penguin Books was a force to contend with. It also gave Allen Lane the opportunity to use colour illustrations in a deluxe series which sold at one shilling a copy. They were the first hard cover Penguin productions, and just as Allen had already used the German Albatross Books and others as prototypes, he now used the German Insel Bucherei, and probably, the Chatto and Windus series called Zodiac Books as models for his King Penguins.

Insel-Bucherei published by Insel Verlag began in Leipzig in 1912. Early Insel-Bucherei were not illustrated but bore the same design throughout. Each had patterned covers derived from 18th century Italian woodblock papers, with a label mounted on the front cover displaying the author, title, and the I-B series number. The text was normally in Gothic black-letter type derived from Schwabacher (so-called Jewscript.) However, on 3rd January 1941 Hitler banned this script in Germany, and thereafter Roman lettering was used. Insel Verlag launched this new series as a rival to Reclam's Universal-Bibliothek, and succeeded admirably in producing a book with very much higher standards of production at a cheaper price. One of the first illustrated I-B was No 281 called "Das Kleine Blumenbuch" by Rudolf Koch and Fritz Kredel, published in 1933. Another one on flowers was "Das Kleine Krauterbuch" by Willi Harwerth, and to compare it with King Penguin 29 and 53, both on flowers, will show the similarities between them. Russell Edwards, in his article "The German Connection" in Penguin Collectors' Society Newsletter No 18, May 1982, states that a third of the King Penguins have a 'pair' in the German series and lists comparable numbers. One other common denominator which the two series had was that, just as King Penguins won many places in the National Book League's annual exhibitions, so Insel-Bucherei won places in "Die Schonsten Deutschen Bucher des Jahres" exhibitions, the German equivalent. The main problem for collectors of the Insel-Bucherei is that, when titles went out of print, their numbers were

King Penguin (K53) June 1950

used for new titles. It therefore makes it difficult to keep track of consecutive titles.

Zodiac Books, which began with Shakespeare's "Lyrics and Shorter Poems", did not use colour illustrations originally, but their format and design are so near to Insel-Bucherei and to King Penguins that, they too should be classed as forerunners to the latter.There were two separate series to Zodiac books;the first ran from 1937-1941 and consisted of twenty-eight volumes. The second began in 1948 and ended in 1951 with number eighteen. Like Insel Bucherei,Chatto and Windus caused confusion by reproducing First Series titles in their Second Series and allocating different numbers.

The first two titles of King Penguins were "British Birds" taken from Gould's "Birds of Britain" (1873), and "A Book of Roses", with illustrations taken from Redoute's "Roses" (1817-1824). They were a triumph, and achieved even greater success with the change of editorship. Elizabeth Senior, originally of the staff of the British Museum, was killed in an air raid after just two years as editor of King Penguins. Her place was taken by Nikolaus Pevsner who, by insisting that R.B. Fishenden, a leading British authority on colour printing, came as joint editor, set up a truly remarkable partnership that resulted in King Penguins being placed on a pinnacle that remains unsurmountable today. The original series ended in 1959 with No 76. During its lifespan it had been awarded twenty-two places in the National Book League's annual exhibitions but rising costs of colour printing eventually made it an uneconomic series.

## Penguin Books in Wartime and the Hatching of Puffins

During the War years dustwrappers were discontinued and all publishers had to reduce the quality of their paper and binding, but Penguin Books produced new series and journals with abandon. Penguin Hansard began in August 1940 and ended six issues later in September 1942; these recorded major speeches in Parliament during the War. In November 1940 another serial was introduced named 'New Writing'. No. 1 was entered as Penguin 305 and became its own numbered periodical which lasted for forty issues until September 1950. Its editor was John Lehmann, and soon this journal was an advertisement for all young authors and artists. As it used original material and was illustrated with special colour supplements, it reflects well the thoughts and viewpoints of that decade.

The first children's books arrived in December 1940. Noel Carrington had been in touch with Allen Lane a year before, seeking sanction to start a new series for children, based on the Soviet illustrated books for children and the Pierre Castor books in Paris. The result was the Puffin Picture Books with titles such as "War on Land" and "War in the Air" which, with their 32 pages of colour and black and white illustrations, easily satisfied a child's endless questions on war. Puffin Picture Book number four was "On The Farm" followed by other titles on subjects such as insects, flowers, pond life, and trains. Each book was factual and beautifully illustrated, always aiming to provide answers for a child's naturally curious mind. These led on naturally to the Puffin Story Books which were in essence a juvenile fiction list. With Eleanor Graham as editor, and her endeavour to produce books that were as near everyday life as possible, Puffin Story Books were always assured of success. The first title, published in December 1941, was Barbara Euphan Todd's "Worzel Gummidge", a character made famous in recent years by television. Fifteen years later in July 1956, this series produced its 100th title, "The Puffin Song Book". A facsimile edition of "Worzel Gummidge" was published in 1981 which celebrated forty years of Puffins and it is prefaced with an article by Eleanor

American Penguin New York 1944

Graham on her years with Penguin Books. Today the Puffin Club exists with thousands of members and the two series are recognised still as having some of the finest titles for juvenile readers. Other children's series that came and went were the Puffin Cut-Out Books which started in 1947, the Baby Puffin Books which made an entrance in November 1943 and an exit in April 1948, and finally the four Porpoise Books published in September 1948.

In June 1941 the Penguin Poets began with a "Selection from Tennyson" by W.E. Williams. This series incorporates Penguin Modern Poets and the many Penguin Books of Verses still in existence today. Penguin Handbooks, which were always designed for the complete beginner, arrived in December 1942, with Raymond Bush's "Soft Fruit Growing". Penguin Reference Books followed a year later in 1943 with E.B. Uvarov's "Dictionary of Science". These abridged versions were not meant for the specialist but for the layman or student needing a handy pocket-size reference book. All these added impetus to the educational books revolution that Penguin had heralded, and have been continued up to the present day.

In December 1941 the first American Penguin made its appearance. To begin with they were reprints of British Penguins but gradually more and more American authors were used. American Penguins, priced at 25 cents had different colour categories to their British counterparts: maroon for novels and plays, yellow for non-fiction, green for crime. The reprints of the British Penguin Specials, with bright orange illustrated covers were called the Fighting Forces and ran from 1942-1945. The Pelican reprints used the prefix P, and twenty-five were published between 1946 and 1948. In 1945 Penguin Books, New York had been an independant firm which maintained the same editorial policy as Penguin Books in England but over the next few years irreparable differences over illustrated covers and choice of authors led to all ties being severed. In 1950 a new American company, Penguin Books Inc. was established at Baltimore, Maryland.

The Forces Book Club was set up in July 1942. A year before,

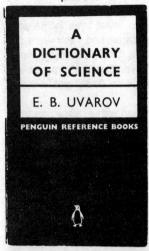

the Canadian Government in Ottawa had asked Penguin Books if they would publish editions exclusively for their armed services. It was Dick Lane who had conducted negotiations and had agreed to be paid with imperial tons of paper instead of money. This was a superb solution to the paper shortage that was the curse of most publishers throughout the War. Allen followed it up in England and as usual managed, where no one else would have, to win approval from the War Office in under 10 months. The agreement stated that Penguin Books would be allocated 60 tons of paper monthly from Paper Control, and that in return they would issue ten titles of the Forces Book Club every month in runs of 75,000. These books were sent to the Allied Forces in Egypt, Italy, France, and many other countries. The authors of these commissioned Penguin or Pelican titles were immediately enthusiastic about their titles being reprinted in this Club edition, which unfortunately finished after a year, and correlative schemes such as the Prisoner of War Services and the Penguin Services Editions. Over and above the additional royalty fee they received, they felt patriotically that they were "doing their bit" for the war. Allen Lane had again proved his forward thinking in setting up this deal because after the War the paper shortage increased and only Penguin Books had the means for mass publication. It was on account of this facility that in 1948 five publishers, Chatto and Windus, Faber & Faber, Hamish Hamilton, Heinemann, and Michael Joseph assigned to Penguin the paperbound reprints rights of several of their best-sellers, thereby augmenting Penguin Books' publicity and prestige at a crucial time.

In wartime, Penguin Books began publishing in French and Italian. The only Italian Penguin, Edizioni del Penguino, "L'Italia di Domani" by Pentad, was published in July 1942. Pentad's book had originally been published as Penguin Special S97 entitled "The Remaking of Italy" in 1941. This book numbered (Q1) is very rare.

In October 1941 the first French Penguin, Editions Pingouin (F1), "Verites sur la France" by Louis Levy, was published and F6, the final number, came out in May 1945. In October 1944

No. 3
*WAR IN THE AIR*
by James Gardner

SIXPENCE

Puffin Picture Book (PP3)
December 1940

(V1), Editions Penguin arrived and this second French series lasted until May 1947, issuing 18 titles which included authors such as Stendhal and Balzac. "Transatlantic", another periodical from Penguin Books whose monthly issues were restricted solely to American matters, began in September 1943 and ended in June 1946.

In April 1944 an exciting new series was initiated, Penguin Modern Painters, under the editorship of Sir Kenneth Clark, which brought home to the public the pleasure of seeing art outside exhibitions and galleries. To many, the great bargain of 32 full-page reproductions of each artists' work at the price of only half-a-crown was too good to miss. Only nineteen were ever published, though it reached MP20 (No 18 was never issued) and, in 1959 it ended, to be replaced eventually by Penguin New Art.

Hubert Phillips, described as a 'One Man Brains Trust', became editor and author of a new series called Ptarmigan Books which began in 1945. These were quiz, problem and puzzle books for all ages. Only nine were ever published and Hubert Phillips assisted in the writing of eight.

In 1945 another two journals arrived, "New Biology" and "Russian Review". The former, edited by Muriel Johnson and her husband M Abercrombie, lasted for 31 issues until 1960, while "Russian Review" only ever had four issues, from October 1945 until January 1948.

# Post-War Series

January 1946 proclaimed the arrival of the Penguin Classics, another of the major successes of Penguin Books. Allen Lane had the amazing knack of getting the right person for the right job against all odds. Dr E.V. Rieu was a retired publisher who had spend most of his life editing school textbooks, yet by translating Homer's "Odyssey" for the Penguin Classics he achieved a recognition impossible in his career in the publishing world. As editor of the Classics Series his aim was to break away from the prosaic and stilted translations of earlier years. He succeeded admirably and his contemporary translation received enthusiastic reviews. By the summer of 1978, 2,255,000 copies of Rieu's "Odyssey" had been sold, and there were over 350 titles in the Classics Series. Each work has been translated by an established writer who can be trusted to produce a work that will satisfy the scholars but will also appeal to the general public.

Between 1946 and 1947 another three serials appeared. The first was "Science News" which ran for fourteen years complete in 54 issues. Its place was taken by "Science Surveys" which was issued from 1960 to 1968 twice annually. The "Film Review", which began in August 1946 and ended with issue nine in August 1949, was the second and it featured many of the foremost cinema critics of the 'Forties'. Another periodical to come at this time from Penguin Books was "Music Magazine", which had only nine numbers too and ended in July 1949. This periodical was edited by Ralph Hill and was primarily written for amateur musicians. Both the "Film Review" and the "Music Magazine" were replaced by Annuals which lasted for a further three years. "The Cinema" 1950, 1951 and 1952 were allocated the Pelican series numbers A226, A233 and A260, while "Music" 1950, 1951 and 1952 had the numbers A225, A232 and A249.

Meanwhile on 26th July 1946 an event occurred which rocked the publishers of London – the first 'Penguin Million'. This was the simultaneous issue of a million books by a single author. On the occasion of his 90th birthday a ten volume set of George Bernard Shaw's works was produced in a million copies. They sold out in

A Penguin Periodical 1947-1949

A Penguin Periodical 1946-1949

Penguin Classics (L1)
January 1946

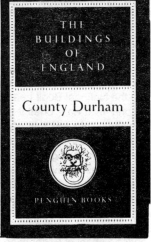

Buildings of England (BE9)
May 1953

just over six weeks. In September 1946 another 'Penguin Million' was published – this time for H.G. Wells to celebrate his 80th birthday, which he unfortunately did not live to see. During the next few years many other authors were honoured in this way including Agatha Christie, Evelyn Waugh and D.H. Lawrence.

Jan Tschichold, a leading book designer and typographer in Europe, was contracted by Allen Lane in 1947 to put the design of Penguin Books in order. He was born in Leipzig in 1902 and, over and above working for most of the major European publishing houses during his lifetime, he was himself the author of many books and articles on different aspects of typography and printing. In the three years he worked for Penguin Books (1947-49) he assisted in the design of almost every series. During the War years standards had naturally dropped, but Jan Tschichold was meticulously thorough in correcting these faults. He was especially concerned with obtaining an improved arrangement of the printed page, using less space between words, and is best remembered for the establishment of the Penguin Composition Rules, still in use today. He also designed a new style for the Pelican Series and other categories such as the Penguin Shakespeare and the Penguin Poets and introduced refinements to the King Penguins. Three of these were No 35, "A Book of Spiders", No 37, "Wild Flowers of the Chalk", and No 38, "Compliments of the Season". In 1949 King Penguin No 8, "Elizabethan Miniatures", was reissued under the directorship of Tschichold and the improvements speak for themselves. A quote from the National Book League states 'As design, cheap books can only rival dear ones if they have a style of their own'. Jan Tschichold initiated this style and in his short stay laid the foundations for future artistic and creative works. Hans Schmoller, a typographic designer who had worked at the Curwen Press previously, succeeded him in 1949 and in the following years concentrated mainly on the cover type and illustration of the Penguin Book. He and his second wife Tatyana, who had been Allen Lane's secretary, later built up a collection of all Penguins published since 1935 and presented it to the London School of Economics. He became a Director of Penguin Books in 1960 and died in September 1985.

Throughout that decade Penguin Books were gaining more influence and this was apparent when Allen Lane was conferred with an honorary MA degree from Bristol University in 1948, and in 1949 E.V. Rieu, editor of the Penguin Classics, received an honorary Litt D from Leeds University.

Under the directorship of J.E. Morpurgo, and with the assistance of Dr Gordon Jacob of the Royal College of Music, Penguin Books produced a new music series entitled Penguin Music Scores in June 1949. Their aim was to supply well-designed booklets, 7 ¾" x 5 ⅛", that would be easily carried in handbags or pockets of concert-goers and would not disturb listeners with the turning over of pages. The first fifteen were oblong while later ones were upright because of scoring technicalities. Each began with twelve pages of text containing a biography of the author and a critical analysis of the work. Priced at half-a-crown each, they proved very popular, the first three titles being, Mozart's Symphony No 40, Bach's Brandenburg Concerto No 3, and Beethoven's "Coriolan and Egmont Overture".

The Pelican History of England was launched with eight specially commissioned titles in February 1950. It started with volume five by S.T. Bindoff on "Tudor England" (A212) and finished with volume one by I.A. Richmond on "Roman Britain" (A315) in April 1955.

The first Penguin Book Exhibition took place at 117 Piccadilly on 21 November 1950 with a display of their 600 stock titles in a plumage of multi-colours. In previous years Penguin Books had participated in the Sunday Times Book Exhibition, but because the promoters could not stage it that year they decided to go it alone and also to donate a percentage of the profits to trade charities. The exhibition at last spurred the press to award Penguin Books the accolade it deserved. The "Times Educational Supplement" wrote 'These guides, prints, classics, poets, modern painters, musical scores and miscellanies suggest that there is no corner of publishing in which a book of low price and good quality cannot find a place' The "New Statesman" wrote: 'But if we are not as ignorant as we were, if

Penguin Books 1000
30th July 1954

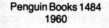
Penguin Books 1484
1960

ONE OF OUR
SUBMARINES

—

EDWARD YOUNG
COMMANDER, D.S.O., D.S.C., R.N.V.(S.)R.

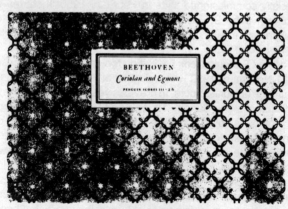

Penguin Music Scores (SC3)
June 1949

indeed something like a revolution has occurred in our reading habits, we probably owe as much to Allen Lane and his advisers as anyone'. The exhibition became an annual event for a number of years.

Vols 1 and 2 of the Buildings of England series were published in July 1951. Its originator was Nikolaus Pevsner who, joined Penguin Books in 1941. Pevsner's dream was to write a number of comprehensive architectural guidebooks covering the whole of England. This he accomplished with stunning success providing scholars and tourists with informative facts in pocket books about the history and architecture of all the churches, monuments, houses and works of art throughout the counties of England. The series consisted of 46 volumes, 32 written by Pevsner himself and the remainder with Pevsner as collaborator. Geoffrey Grigson in his review of the Buildings of England in Penguins Progress 14 summed up this series in these words: 'But in these books a critical scholarly mind with a knowledge shared by few other people of the architecture of Europe is directed onto the finest element of the English scene'. These books, which were usually in hardback, are today one of the most widely collected series and command high prices in second-hand bookshops. This series was not extended to other parts of Britain until 1978, when a volume on the buildings of Lothian was published; but most of Scotland, Wales and Northern Ireland has yet to be covered.

However Nikolaus Pevsner is also remembered as the originator of the Pelican History of Art which began in 1953, one of the first cloth bound productions. It was to be a comprehensive history of world art in the English language. This was a deluxe series printed on luxury paper containing 300 text pages and with around 300 half-tone illustrations. At two guineas a volume these books were larger, 10 ½" by 7 ¼" and four were issued annually until the series was complete in 48 volumes. Together with the Penguin Modern Painters and Penguin Prints which had started in 1948 as folder reproductions of great paintings, these books filled a gap in the fine art market for supply to universities, schools and libraries for many years.

The first of the Penguin Books devoted to African affairs was published in October 1953. The West African Series began with Ronald Wraith's book on "Local Government", but by the time D. Austen's book on "West Africa and the Commonwealth" entered as WA7, the front cover name had been changed to just the African Series. The series ended in 1965 with number fourteen, though other series followed: the Penguin African Library, which began in 1962 and the Pelican series, African Affairs.

The Penguin series reached number 1,000 in July 1954 and to mark this event they published a specially designed reprint of "One of our Submarines" by Edward Young. This was the same man who as an office junior had been sent to the zoo to sketch penguins and subsequently produced the first logo for Penguin Books. In August of the same year the Pelican History of the World began with K.S. Latourette, "A History of Modern China" (A302).

Penguin Books celebrated its coming of age in July 1956 and Puffin Story Books reached their century with "The Puffin Song Book". W.E. Williams, who had been with the firm for 20 years, wrote "The Penguin Story,1935-1956", the first of many historical accounts of Penguin Books including a useful list of all the books published up to that date. In the same month Allen Lane was Knighted and it is said by his friends that on hearing the advance news of the honour he took to his bed for 24 hours in total disbelief!

The final periodical, "Science Surveys", a bi-annual publication, began in 1960 and ended eight years later. This was Penguin Books' last venture into their own journal production. Various reasons for this have been put forward, but basically infrequency of issues and inconsistency of publishing schedules led to their downfall. From 1947 the Penguin Serials became officially known as "Penguin Occasionals". Finally, from 1950 onwards, journal publishing became a major concern internationally. Firms became solely dedicated to their production, causing a flood of material available in every subject possible, and Penguin Books realised they could no longer make a strong impression in this field.

## 1960: Twenty-Five Years of Penguin Books

In 1960 a number of remarkable events took place. Firstly, of course, July marked the Silver Jubilee of Penguin Books, and to celebrate it,"Penguins Progress, 1935-1960", was published in September and listed under the number Q25 ('Q' was used for books that did not fit into any special category or series and by 1960 had reached Q36). The book was designed by Hans Schmoller and included articles by Richard Hoggart and Compton Mackenzie. The foreword was by Sir Allen Lane and included a potted biography of him and other prominent Penguin people. Edinburgh University Library would be delighted to acquire a copy of this to add to our collection.

Secondly on 20 October 1960 the case against Penguin Books for publishing the unexpurgated edition of "Lady Chatterley's Lover" by D.H. Lawrence opened at the Old Bailey. Allen Lane's decision to include this book in the "Lawrence Million" on the 30th anniversary of his death was quite understandable. It was a reprint of a famous novel and it had never been produced as a paperback or as a Penguin. What he failed to foresee was that the authorities were itching for a test case for the Obscene Publications Act of 1959. However, showing his usual excellent judgment and opportunism, he refused to withdraw the book. He not only fought the charge and won with world publicity 14 days later, but by February 1961 had published the transcript of the infamous case, "The Trial of Lady Chatterley".

Lastly, Tony Godwin on Allen Lane's invitation joined the staff of Penguin Books as an editorial adviser in 1960. He had made his mark originally in the bookselling world and he soon showed his worth by being promoted very quickly to Fiction Editor and then Chief Editor.

On 20 April 1961 Penguin Books had become a public company with shares going up 6d within one day. However this could not stop the steady decline, and by 1964 it was evident that the firm would be forced to reduce drastically its publishing programmes and reorganise its staff. W.E. Williams retired at this time. Penguin Books had become rather self-satisfied in the

Sixties, allowing its rivals, such as Pan Books, to snatch up popular authors and produce such best sellers as "The Dam Busters", "Colditz Story" and others. Content that companies had been founded in the United States of America, Canada and Australia, with agencies worldwide, Allen Lane dismissed the portents of the new paperback revolution. In America the New American Library founded by Kurt Enoch (remembered for the Albatross paperbacks) was firmly established, and in Britain Pan Books , which began in 1947, had captured a large part of the sales market. Tony Godwin eventually left in 1967 after many arguments with Allen Lane, but in his short stay he had almost tripled the annual turnover, and his extravagant but decisive buying had brought new authors and titles into Penguin Books.

# The End of an Era

Allen Lane was admitted to Middlesex Hospital with cancer of the bowel in 1968, and during the following two years his health steadily deteriorated. He spent most of his time between his home at Priory Farm, near Reading, and the radiography department of the hospital. He would go into Harmondsworth perhaps twice a week and it was in this period that he began his negotiations with Pearson Longman for a merger.

Allen Lane died on 7 July 1970 after being in a coma for seven days; the next day there was an announcement from Penguin Books that a merger was imminent with the Pearson Longman Group. This event took place on 21 August of the same year. For the next few years Penguin Books went into the worst decline of its history, until in 1979 there was a trading loss of £400,000. Much of this was due to inflation, forcing production and operation costs to almost double, but the main reason was that Penguin Books had always made their money because of small profits and large turnover. The small profits were continuing but there was no longer the same demand for Penguins. Peter Mayer was brought in to save the Company and as Tony Godwin had done earlier he doubled the turnover within a year. Since then Penguin Books have gone from strength to strength, culminating in April 1985 when they bought Michael Joseph, Hamish Hamilton and other imprints. Today they have a massive back list of 6,000 titles in print and every year over 40 million books roll off their presses.

Fifty years on, in 1985, the ratio of hardbacks to paperbacks in publishing programmes is round 60:40. Over and above the obvious reasons, production costs and cheaper prices for the public, plus the format attraction to the purchasers, the changing patterns of publishers and libraries have accelerated its acceptance. Increasingly some titles are only available in paperbacks, especially with minority presses, eg Pluto, etc. Many paperbacks now are sewn and printed on a better quality paper, while occasionally adhesives are used on hardbacks, a complete reversal of the customary practice. Many people believe that the quality of hardcover books has deteriorated, while the quality of paperbacks is improving with every production. Innovations in binding have produced Lyfeguards (durable plastic covers in every size) which cover the paperback, protecting its covers and spine from tearing and grubbiness. These only cost 35p-40p, whereas previous library practice necessitated paperbacks to be bound in cloth at the minimum price of £3.00-£4.00. In academic libraries such as Edinburgh University Library, therefore, it makes sound sense, especially in the face of severe financial restraints in the past few years, to buy two or three paperback copies for the price of one hardback. This is especially true when purchasing multiple copies for undergraduate Reading Rooms. Protected by a Lyfeguard, a softbound copy can last a considerable length of time. Additionally, with the growing problem of mutilation of books, it is more economical to replace with a low cost paperback than xerox missing pages and rebind. Penguin books continue to be among the most popular paperbacks in social sciences, literature and classics and are therefore now bought by many libraries. Fifty years on, publishers, libraries and scholars view the paperback with different eyes as a useful, beneficial and lasting development.

Allen Lane was once asked by the BBC what he classed as the greatest compliment ever paid to him. He replied that it was when the BBC said that 'Penguin Books have been the greatest popular educators in our generation'. Clement Attlee is quoted as saying to J.E. Morpurgo that 'his path to Downing Street was paved with Penguins'. Famous quotations from a thousand more admirers could be repeated but my favourite is Allen Lane's own one which he often repeated – that his success was due to the fact that he was 'a cross between a missionary and a mercenary'. I think that sums up his qualities admirably. He was never an intellectual but, through his charm and persuasive tongue, surrounded himself with leading academics in every field. His aim was to provide for everyone the knowledge he himself had been starved of, written in a way that was easily understood but which excluded condescension. To say that he reached his goal is a gross understatement because in doing so he compelled everyone else, his advisors, his readers, his authors and friends, into fulfilling their secret ambitions too.

## Chronological Events

|  |  |  |
|---|---|---|
|  | 1837 | Christian Bernhard Tauchnitz founded his company Berhn. Tauchnitz Jun. in Leipzig |
| 21st September | 1902 | Allen Lane Williams born |
| 16th April | 1919 | Allen Lane Williams changes his name by deed poll to Allen Lane |
| 23rd April | 1919 | Allen Lane joins the Bodley Head |
| February | 1925 | John Lane dies |
|  | 1926 | Sheed & Ward Publishing Company formed |
|  | 1926 | Sheed and Ward, Publishers, founded |
|  | 1930 | Allen Lane becomes Chairman of the Bodley Head |
|  | 1932 | The first Albatross Paperback published |
| 30th July | 1935 | First ten Penguins issued |
| October | 1935 | Numbers 11-20 of Penguin Books published |
| 1st January | 1936 | Penguin Books Ltd. founded with a capital of £100. The three directors were brothers Allen, Richard and John Lane |
|  | 1936 | Tauchnitz and Albatross merge |
| April | 1937 | First six Penguin Shakespeare Books launched – completed in 1959 |
| May | 1937 | First Pelican published – G.B. Shaw: "The Intelligent Woman's Guide to Socialism" |
| 4th August | 1937 | Allen Lane's father lays the foundation stone at Harmondsworth |
| November | 1937 | First Penguin Special – Edgar Mowrer: "Germany Puts the Clock Back" |
|  | 1937 | Chatto & Windus publishes the First Zodiac Book |
| November | 1937 | Penguin Parade I issued as Penguin No.120 then becomes first journal |
|  | 1937 | The Bodley Head goes into voluntary liquidation |

| | | |
|---|---|---|
| May | 1938 | Nos.1-10 Penguin Illustrated Classics published |
| March | 1939 | First Penguin Guide printed |
| November | 1939 | King Penguin One and Two published |
| August | 1940 | Penguin Hansard begins – ended with number H6 in September 1942 |
| November | 1940 | Penguin New Writing – ended in September 1950 |
| December | 1940 | Puffin Picture Books, Penguin's first books solely for children |
| 31st December | 1940 | German bomb raid wipes out most of London's Publishing Houses |
| | 1941 | Nikolaus Pevsner joins Penguin Books Ltd. |
| June | 1941 | Penguin Poets |
| December | 1941 | Puffin Story Books |
| April | 1942 | Planning Design and Art books |
| December | 1942 | Penguin Handbooks |
| April | 1943 | Penguin Reference books |
| September | 1943 | Transatlantic Serial issued – ended in June 1946 |
| November | 1943 | Baby Puffin Books – ended in April 1948 |
| 3rd December | 1943 | Tauchnitz Publishing Company, Leipzig, wiped out by air-raid |
| May | 1944 | First six Penguin Modern Painters launched. |
| July | 1945 | Ptarmigan Books. They lasted until November 1947 |
| July | 1945 | New Biology – ended with Issue 31 in 1960 |
| October | 1945 | Russian Review begins – ended in February 1948 |
| December | 1945 | E.V. Rieu joins Penguin Books Ltd. |
| January | 1946 | Penguin Classics launched with E.V. Rieu's translation of Homer's "Odyssey" |
| 20th May | 1946 | Tauchnitz Edition GMBH founded in Hamburg by Christian Wegner |

| June | 1946 | Science News – ended with Issue 54 in 1960 |
|---|---|---|
| 26th July | 1946 | First Penguin Million – G.B. Shaw |
| August | 1946 | Film review begins – ceased publication in August 1949 |
| September | 1946 | Second Penguin Million – H.G. Wells |
| | 1947 | Jan Tschichold joins Penguin Books Ltd |
| February | 1947 | Music Magazine launched – ended in July 1949 |
| June | 1947 | The Things We See published until May 1953 |
| December | 1947 | Puffin Cut-out Books – ceased in October 1953 |
| | 1948 | Allen Lane conferred with an Honorary M.A. degree from Bristol University |
| | 1948 | Five publishers assign the paper-bound reprint rights of several of their bestsellers |
| September | 1948 | The only four Porpoise Books published |
| December | 1948 | Penguin Prints – ended in 1952 |
| | 1949 | E.V. Rieu conferred with an Honorary degree Litt.D. from Leeds University |
| | 1949 | Jan Tschichold leaves Penguin Books Ltd and is succeeded by Hans Schmoller. |
| June | 1949 | Penguin Music Scores edited by Dr Gordon Jacob. |
| September | 1950 | Pelican History of England launched with Volume 5 relating to Tudor England |
| 21st November | 1950 | The first Penguin Book Exhibition takes place at 117 Piccadilly |
| July | 1951 | The Buildings of England Nos.1 & 2 published |
| May | 1953 | Pelican History of Art Volumes 1 & 2, the first cloth-bound series issued from Penguin Books Ltd. |
| October | 1953 | West African Penguins |
| July | 1956 | Twenty-one year anniversary of Penguin Books Ltd. |

| | | |
|---|---|---|
| July | 1956 | W.E. Williams writes "The Penguin Story 1935-1956" |
| July | 1956 | "The Puffin Song Book" published to celebrate the 100th Puffin Story Book |
| July | 1956 | Allen Lane knighted |
| | 1960 | Science surveys begin – ended in 1968 |
| | 1960 | Penguin Books prosecuted for publishing the unexpurgated edition of Lady Chatterley's Lover by D.H. Lawrence |
| | 1960 | D.H. Lawrence million launched on the 30th anniversary of his death |
| | 1960 | Tony Godwin becomes Chief Editor |
| July | 1960 | Silver Jubilee of Penguin Books Ltd. |
| July | 1960 | "Penguins Progress 1935-1960" written |
| 20th April | 1961 | Penguin Books Ltd. becomes a Public Company when 690,000 shares are offered at 12/- a share |
| | 1965 | W.E. Williams retires from the Penguin Board after thirty years service |
| | 1967 | Allen Lane begins discussions with Pearson Longman |
| | 1967 | The Puffin Club founded |
| | 1967 | Tony Godwin leaves Penguin |
| | 1968 | Allen Lane admitted to Middlesex Hospital with cancer of the bowel |
| 23rd April | 1969 | Golden Jubilee of Allen Lane's entry into publishing |
| June | 1969 | Queen makes Allen Lane a Companion of Honour |
| 7th July | 1970 | Allen Lane dies |
| 8th July | 1970 | Announcement that merger was imminent with Pearson Longman |
| 21st August | 1970 | Penguin Books Ltd. merged with the Pearson Longmann Group |
| 8th February | 1973 | Bernhard Tauchnitz Verlag – struck off register because of lack of capital |
| | 1974 | Penguin Collectors' Society founded |

| | 1979 | Penguin Books has a trading loss of £400,000 |
| | 1979 | Peter Mayer, well-versed in America's paperback publishing, brought in to turn the tide |
| | 1984 | Penguin Books has sales of £50 million |
| April | 1985 | Penguin Books buys Michael Joseph, Hamish Hamilton and several other colophons |
| 30th July | 1985 | Golden Jubilee of Penguin Books |
| 5th September | 1985 | 50th year anniversary celebrations begin |

# Penguin Collection at Edinburgh University Library

Edinburgh University Library accepted a large bequest of over 1,500 books from by Mr K.S. Ryrie in 1979. A former graduate of science of Edinburgh University, he had worked in Ferranti's Edinburgh, for over 30 years. He had been a compulsive reader, and his collection reflected his diverse interests. Part of it consisted of 500 early Penguins and Pelicans. The Acquisitions Librarian at that time, Mr Derek Law, had noticed a renewed interest in Penguin Books and also a Christie's Catalogue offering a collection of 2,000 Penguin Books for sale at a considerable price. The decision was made to keep these paperbacks as a unit and Kenneth Ryrie's donation formed the nucleus of our collection which has now grown to 450 Pelicans from A1-A500 and 1,300 Penguins from 1-1,500. From 1979 this has been a much enjoyed additional responsibility, and my position as Donations Librarian has given me great opportunities to add to our collection. Most prospective donors are surprised but delighted to give these paperbacks and we have had a great response from appeals to our staff and to the Friends of Edinburgh University Library. With the advent of the computer all wanted titles are listed and therefore easily run-off for all people who wish to assist in supplying the missing numbers. At many jumble sale bookstalls in Edinburgh you will see myself or other helpers clutching these computer lists. A member of the University staff, Dr Angus Mitchell, became our first "swapper" of duplicates and put me in touch with the Penguin Collectors Society. All our duplicates are on computer file and these along with our "Wants" Lists are available to any person who writes to:

Mrs Sally Wood
Donations Librarian
Edinburgh University Library
George Square
Edinburgh
EH8 9LJ

Though we began by collecting only Penguins, Pelicans, Penguin Specials and Classics, other items which will complement our own special fields are now being sought. For example Penguin New Writing would greatly enhance our "Thirties" literature archives featuring Evelyn Waugh, W.H. Auden, etc. The Film Review and Music Magazine would be prized additions to our cinema and music collections, while the Guides would be very useful to our extensive map holdings. The Illustrated Classics plus the Penguin Shakespeares would be welcomed in our standard holdings of the authors in question. We would also like to acquire a complete set of King Penguins, as we only have a few, and a set of illustrated Insel Bucherei as examples of early colour printing. Lastly we would like to obtain a complete run of Penguins Progress and Penguin Collectors Society Newsletters 1-17, as both give valuable and rare information into the development and organisation of Penguin Books series. Our collection runs from 1935-1960 and we hope we might be able to complete it before 1990.

# Penguin Collectors' Society

The Penguin Collectors' Society was formed in 1974 by a 'small group of enthusiasts'. The first secretary was David Hall and the first editors were Andrew Hajducki and A.S. Atchison. The original meeting was held in Richmond and on the publication date of the first Penguin Collectors' Society Newsletter the membership stood at thirty-eight. Current membership is over 400 with subscribers in the United States of America, Canada, Australia, Zimbabwe and the Netherlands. The Penguin Collectors Society Newsletter is published twice a year in May and November with a subscription cost of £3.50 per annum, £4.50 overseas,and consists of excellent articles on selected Penguin series. It provides information that is essential for all Penguin collectors and in Newsletter 23 there is also on pp21-22 a comprehensive index to these articles. In every issue there are sections entitled "Penguin Advertiser" and "Penguin Notes and Comments".The former lists, free of charge, members' "wants", duplicates and exchanges while the latter is an important guide to the idiosyncrasies of Penguin Books and solves many unanswered queries.. The Newsletters always contain a list of new members plus occasional reviews of relevant articles or books.

Finally, a number of "Penguin Trails" have been featured which centre on a specific town listing all bookshops that are worth a visit to procure Penguin Books. I have found these Newsletters invaluable in my research for this booklet and also in the supervision of the Library's collection. Anyone who would like more information should write to the current Secretary at the following address:

> Mr Anthony Sidell
> 33 Patmore Link Road
> Leverstock Green
> Hemel Hempstead
> Herts

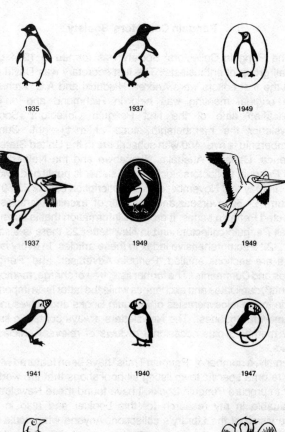

**Some early and current devices**

# Bibliography

## Journal Articles

UNWIN, Stanley. *Concerning sixpennies* in Times Literary Supplement. 19 November 1938. p.737

COLE, Margaret. *Books for the people* in Times Literary Supplement, 26 November 1938. p.751

*TEN YEARS OF PENGUINS.* Penguin Books 1945. in The Bookseller. 23 August, 6 September, 13 September, 1945.

Various articles in Penguins Progress Nos.2-5, 7-11, 13-14. 1946-51.

CARRINGTON, Noel. *A century for Puffin Picture Books* in Penrose Annual, 1957. pp.62-64

SPENCER, Herbert. *Penguins on the march* in Typographica (New Series) No.5. June 1962.

GRAHAM, Eleanor. *Puffin Books* in Signal Magazine. September 1973. pp.115-122

HALL, D.J. *Penguin collectors' story* in Antiquarian Book Monthly Review. v.5. September 1978. pp.360-367

TODD, W.B. *Firma Tauchnitz: a further investigation* in Publishing History. v.2. 1978. pp.7-26

MORPURGO, J.E. *The King and I* in Blackwoods Magazine. December 1979. pp.477-487

PRESSLER, K.H. *The Tauchnitz edition, beginning and end of a famous series* in Publishing History. v.6. 1979/80. pp.62-78

SWIFT, K. *First Penguin proof* in Antiquarian Book Monthly Review. v.8. January 1981. pp.16-17

MCLEAN, R. *Collecting books for their design. pt.1. Cheap editions before Penguins hatched* in Antiquarian Book Monthly Review. v.8. 1981. pp.224-227

McLEAN, R. *Penguins planned by Tschichold* in Antiquarian Book Monthly Review. v.8. August 1981. pp.292-295

BERRY, J. & MILLER, K. *Preference for paperbacks – an L.J. mini-survey* in Library Journal. v.106. No.16. 15 September 1981. pp.1687-1691

EDWARDS, Russell. *The German connection* in Penguin Collectors' Society. Newsletter. No.18. May 1982. pp.234-241

HART, M. *Paperback – mostly pros and few cons in hard times* in Library Association Record. v.85(5) 1983. pp.187-189

McGARVA, Duncan. *The Penguin periodicals, rise and fall* in Penguin Collectors' Society Newsletter. No.20. June 1983 pp.313-316

EDWARDS, Russell. *Short and sweet: illustrated classics* in Penguin Collectors' Society Newsletter. No.21. November 1983. pp.6-8

JACKSON, K. *Collecting Penguins* in Book and Magazine Collector. March 1984. pp.18-25

EDWARDS, Russell. *Insel books* in Antiquarian Book Monthly Review. v.11. April 1984. pp.18-25

EDWARDS, Russell. *The mysterious affair at Harmondsworth: missing titles and numbers* in Penguin Collectors' Society Newsletter. No.23. 1984. pp.15-19

RUSSELL, T. *Half a century of Penguin* in The Listener. June 1985. pp.13-15

HOLLOWAY, D. *The day of the Penguin* in The Daily Telegraph. Saturday, 13 July 1985.


**Books and Pamphlets**

YOUNG, E. *One of our submarines.* Penguin Books No.1000. 1954. (Article entitled *Penguins, a retrospect.* pp.I-VIII.)

WILLIAMS, Sir W.E. *Penguin story 1935-1956.* Penguin Books. 1956.

FLOWER, Desmond. *The paperback: its past, present and future.* Privately circulated 1959.

*PENGUINS PROGRESS.* 1935-1960 – printed on silver jubilee of Penguin Books. Penguin Books. 1960.

WILLIAMS Sir W.E. *Allen Lane: a personal portrait.* Bodley Head. 1973. (ISBN 0 370 104749)

MORPURGO, J.E. *Allen Lane – King Penguin.* London. 1979. (ISBN 0 09 139690 5)

SCHMOLLER, Hans. *The Paperback revolution* in
  BRIGGS, Asa: *Essays in the history of publishing*. pp.283-318. London. 1974. (ISBN 0 582 36521)
GREEN, Evelyne. *Penguin Books, the pictorial cover 1960-1980*. Manchester Polytechnic Library 1981
SCHREUDERS, Piet. *The Book of paperbacks*, translated by Josh Pachter. Virgin Books. London. 1981. (ISBN 0 90 7080 19)
BISHOP, Diana. *King Penguins; their place in 20th century publishing*. Penguin Collectors' Society. 1982.
*MUMBY'S publishing and bookselling in 20th century,* by Ian Norrie. 6th edition. London. 1982. (ISBN 0 7135 1341 1)
TSCHICHOLD, Jan. *Typographer and type designer 1902-1974.* Catalogue of exhibition held in the National Library of Scotland, Edinburgh 1982. (ISBN 0 90222 0535)
CHERRY, Bridget. *The Buildings of England.* Penguin Collectors' Society. 1983. (ISBN 0 90704-9060)
CHIDLEY, John. *Discovering book collecting.* 1983. (ISBN 0 85263 5885)
WILLIAMS, R.A.H. *British Paperback Checklists 1-6.*
  R.A.H. Williams Bookseller, Scunthorpe. n.d.